Foreword

This book is aimed at t
allergies (such as asthn   or
made worse by breathir   1
plants to choose for your   ρuʉen or
low pollen) in order to rec   ,espiratory allergies. It
also tells you about other k .ں of plant allergies (food allergies
and plant contact allergies) – why we get them, what happens
in our bodies, how pathologists diagnose them and what
treatments are available. We have written this book in response
to a request from Her Majesty the Queen. We presented an
exhibit of plants known to be associated with respiratory
allergies in our Chelsea Flower Show display in 2012. Her
Majesty asked if there was a book she could read about
allergies, plants and pathology diagnosis. When we said there
was not, she suggested we write one. So, here it is!

Tim Wreghitt explains the 2012 Royal College of Pathologists' Chelsea Flower
Show exhibit to HM The Queen

Low Allergy Gardening
The why and how of plant allergies and plants to choose for your low allergy garden

Dr Joanna Sheldon PhD, FRCPath

Consultant Clinical Scientist
St George's Hospital, London

Dr Tim Wreghitt OBE, BSc, MA, PhD, FRCPath

Consultant Clinical Scientist
Addenbrooke's Hospital, Cambridge

Published by The Royal College of Pathologists

The Royal College of Pathologists
Pathology: the science behind the cure

www.rcpath.org

First published in Great Britain in 2016
by The Royal College of Pathologists

Copyright © The Royal College of Pathologists,
Dr Joanna Sheldon and Dr Tim Wreghitt.

The moral rights of the authors has been asserted.

Picture credits: The plant photographs remain the copyright © of:

Mr Clive Nichols:
Pages: 5, 8, 11, 13, 15, 16, 20, 21, 26, 39, 41, 46,
50, 58, 59, 61, 62, 64, 66, 68, 69, 74, 78 ,79

Dr Henry Oakeley:
Pages: 25, 29, 31, 34, 35, 38, 44, 51, 53,
54, 56, 57, 60, 65, 70, 73, 75, 77

Designed by Lorraine Brown, Red Graphic Cambridge Ltd. www.redgraphic.co.uk

ISBN 978-1-5262-0306-9

Printed and bound in Great Britain

Acknowledgements

We are extremely grateful to Dr Suzy Lishman (Royal College of Pathologists'
President) and Dr David Bailey (Royal College of Pathologists' Vice President for
Communications) for supporting this book and for helpful editing. We are also
indebted to Clive Nichols (www.clivenichols.com) and to Dr Henry Oakeley
(Garden Fellow at The Royal College of Physicians) for generously providing plant
images (The Royal College of Physicians medicinal garden website:
http://garden.rcplondon.ac.uk). Dr Michael Perkin (Consultant in Paediatric
Allergy and Honorary Clinical Research Fellow, St George's, University of London)
kindly performed the skin testing shown in Chapter 2. We would also like to
thank Lorraine Brown of Red Graphic for her help in publishing the book.

All plants used
within this book,
are plants to
choose if you want
to create a Low
allergy garden

Lamium
Photographer: Clive Nichols

Iris sibirica
Photographer: Clive Nichols

Chapter One

What is allergy?

Chapter One

What is allergy?

The immune system has an extraordinary method of recognising small amounts of chemicals (usually proteins) on the surface of everything that we encounter, typically through our lungs, gut and across our skin. These chemicals can be on the surface of infectious agents like bacteria or viruses. The immune system is vital in recognising these infections and mounting an immune response to destroy them. There are also chemicals that are part of our day-to-day life, in the foods we eat, from the animals that share our houses and in the trees and plants that we encounter. The immune system recognises these things but has learned that they are not harmful and to ignore them. Sometimes, the immune system gets the signals wrong and makes a response to things that are not in themselves harmful e.g. pollen or peanuts. These inappropriate immune responses are called allergies. The end result of this immune response is inflammation, which we recognise as hot, red, swollen and painful tissues. When we are talking about allergies, we experience this, for example, as sore red, itchy nose or eyes.

"Allergen" is the general name we use for the things that cause allergies. The most common allergens are pollens and animal dander but foods, drugs and insects are also important allergens.

Allergy is widespread and affects approximately one in four of the population in the UK at some time in their lives. Each year the numbers are increasing and as many as half of all people affected by allergy are children. The symptoms of allergy and their severity vary between people and even in one person over time. The main symptoms of allergy are shown in the table.

Symptoms of allergy

- Headache,
- Red, itchy and swollen eyes (conjunctivitis)
- Coughing, wheezing, breathlessness, asthma
- Runny nose, sneezing, red and itchy nose (rhinitis)
- Tummy ache or abdominal pain
- Vomiting
- Diarrhoea
- Red, dry itchy skin (eczema or atopic dermatitis)
- Red, raised itchy bumps on the skin (nettle rash, hives, urticaria)
- Throat swelling
- Drop in blood pressure
- Circulatory shock
- Collapse
- Chest tightness
- Anaphylactic shock

Geranium
Photographer: Clive Nichols

Rhinitis and hay fever

Rhinitis is the medical name for inflammation of the membranes lining the nose and throat; it can be caused by infection, a reaction to medication, irritation by dusts, or by allergies. Patients with rhinitis may have other symptoms like red and itchy eyes, blocked nose and blocked sinuses. Rhinitis is often regarded as a trivial problem but studies have shown that it severely affects people's quality of life. It disturbs sleep, impairs daytime concentration and the ability to carry out tasks, causes people to miss work or school, and has been shown to affect children's school exam results. People who suffer from rhinitis are at increased risk of developing asthma. Inflammation at the beginning of the airway (the nose) frequently proceeds to involve the lower airways leading to the lungs, and this has led to the "one airway" approach to treatment. Many asthmatics also suffer from rhinitis. If this is treated effectively, their asthma is better controlled and they have fewer A&E attendances and hospital admissions.

Allergic rhinitis is the term used when a person has an allergic reaction to a substance such as pollen, house dust mites, animals or pets including birds, or moulds. Hay fever is the general name that we give to allergic reactions (including rhinitis) to pollens.

Asthma

Asthma is the medical name given to breathing problems that are caused by narrowing of the airways (the tubes that lead to the lungs). This narrowing can be caused by infection or allergies. When the airways narrow, it is more difficult to get air in and out of the lungs and patients feel tightness in their chests and are breathless. People may also have a dry irritating cough and

Eryngium x tripartitum
Photographer: Clive Nichols

may wheeze when they breathe. Allergens like house dust mites or pets and grass or tree pollens are common triggers for asthma. Infections like colds can also act as triggers. There are also non-specific irritants that can make the asthma symptoms worse. These include cigarette smoke, car exhaust fumes, perfumes, aerosol sprays, change in temperature (especially going from a warm to a cold environment), paint fumes, cooking odours and exercise.

Anaphylaxis

Anaphylaxis is the most severe allergic reaction that is life-threatening if not treated rapidly. Symptoms include swelling of the airways and breathing difficulties, a rapid fall in blood pressure and a rash all over the body.

What are the important components of an allergic reaction?

The important components of an allergic reaction are the allergen, an antibody called IgE, mast cells and inflammatory chemicals or mediators. Allergic reactions happen when an allergen (typically a protein) is recognised by the body's immune system as foreign. There are many ways that the body can respond. In allergic reactions, the antibody called IgE, that is exactly the right "shape" for the allergen. It is made by a component of the immune system called B cells. The IgE sticks onto the surface of mast cells and these are now primed and ready to respond next time the same allergen is encountered. Mast cells are packed full of chemical substances, such as histamine that have potent inflammatory effects. The release of these substances is what causes the symptoms of allergy.

Allergens

An allergen is any substance that can cause an allergic reaction. Many things that we encounter in our normal lives have the potential to be allergens e.g. the foods that we eat, the animals that share our houses and the trees and grasses that we plant in our gardens. There are hundreds of different allergens and the main groups are shown in the table:

Groups of allergens

- Grass pollens
- Tree pollens
- Weed pollens
- Drugs
- Skin and animal proteins
- Foods of plant origin
- Foods of animal origin
- House dust and dust mites
- Insects
- Mites
- Moulds
- Parasites
- Venoms
- Occupational allergens

Iris sibirica
Photographer: Clive Nichols

Scabiosa caucasica
Photographer: Clive Nichols

Pollen

Pollen is the most important allergen when thinking about allergies related to gardening. Plants produce pollen as part of their reproductive cycle. The pollen can be spread from one plant to another by the wind or by insects. Wind pollinated plants produce the most pollen - for example every flower cluster or catkin of a birch tree contains approximately six million pollen grains and releases over five billion in a season.

Pollen grains usually contain only a few cells which are surrounded by a coating that can be smooth or covered with pores or spines or ridges. Pollen grains photographed under a microscope can be beautiful.

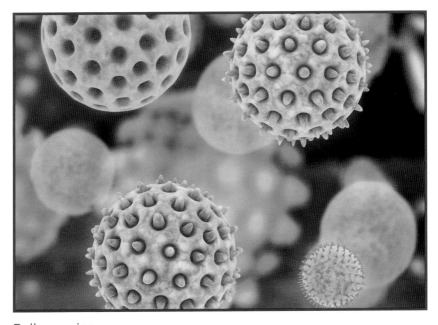

Pollen grains

Chapter One

When we say someone has an allergic reaction to pollen, they are not actually reacting to the whole pollen grain but to tiny amounts of protein components on its coating. There is no single characteristic that makes these components allergenic although certain structures (e.g. specific sequences of the building blocks that make proteins or regions where other molecules are added) and functions are common features of allergens. There are similarities between the allergens which can mean that people who are sensitive to one type of pollen may respond to another type of pollen due to cross-reactivity. Information can be found, which includes a description and geographical distribution of the plant, specific details of the allergen, cross reactivity and clinical experience, all supported by references from the scientific literature. http://www.phadia.com/en-GB/5/Products/ImmunoCAP-Allergens

The time of the year that plants are in flower is very predictable. Trees first come into flower in January and finish in late April. Grasses flower in late spring and weeds in summer. Within the group there is also a typical order in which plants come into flower. For example hazel trees flower before birch trees. The pollen calendar is very useful to help identify what plants are in flower at any one time and what group of plants a person is reacting to.

The pollen calendar can be found on page 35

Immunoglobulin E (IgE)

Immune responses are a complex sequence of events involving many different types of cell in the body and chemical substances responding to an antigen (anything that generates an immune response). A type of cell called a T lymphocyte stimulates and organises the immune response and helps to generate the most appropriate selection of proteins and cells to help recognise and defend the body against that antigen in the future. We actually make immune responses to everything that we encounter in our lives but generally we ignore the things that are not harmful or that we see regularly.

Immunoglobulins are proteins that are the most important recognition molecules of the immune system. They are made by B cells. An immunoglobulin called IgG is vital in identifying and destroying things that may cause us harm by infection, such as bacteria or viruses. Immunogobulin E (IgE) is important in defending us against parasites but it is also involved in allergic reactions.

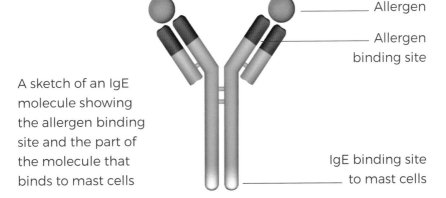

Allergen

Allergen binding site

A sketch of an IgE molecule showing the allergen binding site and the part of the molecule that binds to mast cells

IgE binding site to mast cells

Vinca minor
Photographer: Clive Nichols

Hosta
Photographer: Clive Nichols

The first time that a person makes an immune response to an allergen that they have encountered is called the sensitisation stage. We encounter the allergens most often across our mucosal surfaces e.g. respiratory tract or gut. Our genetic make-up, the allergen or antigen and what other things our immune system is reacting to all determine the type of immune response that we make. Certain groups of antigens, usually those that are not in themselves dangerous, push the immune system to make IgE. Once someone has made IgE to a particular allergen, they have been sensitised to the allergen and have the potential to respond to the allergen the next time they encounter it. Some people may be sensitised to an allergen but can be in contact with it without any symptoms.

Some people develop allergies later in life, having previously encountered the allergen without any symptoms. Scientists don't fully understand why this happens. Nor do we know why some allergens seem to be more potent than others or why different people respond to different allergens. What we do know is that IgE sticks onto the surface of mast cells and these become sensitised and ready to respond the next time the person encounters the allergen.

Mast cells

Mast cells sit in tissues, particularly those that are in contact with the external environment, including the skin, nose, eyes, mouth, throat, stomach and gut. If you look at a mast cell under a microscope, you will see that it has many tiny "bubbles" or granules which contain a variety of chemicals including histamine. When a mast cell coated with IgE specific to an allergen meets the allergen again, a cascade of signals makes the mast cell release the inflammatory chemicals. This may be in only one area of the body e.g. the nose so the symptoms are very localised or it may also be a widespread reaction or a severe anaphylactic reaction. The release of the mediators happens very quickly (within seconds or minutes) after the allergen comes into contact with sensitised mast cells and it is the release of these chemicals from mast cells that causes increase in blood flow, blood vessel permeability, mucous secretion, smooth muscle irritability and hot red, itchy and sometimes painful tissues. These are all part of the inflammatory response and generate the allergic symptoms that we recognise. We are most familiar with histamine as the chemical involved in allergic reactions but there are others including enzymes e.g. tryptase, serotonin and prostaglandins.

Mast cell

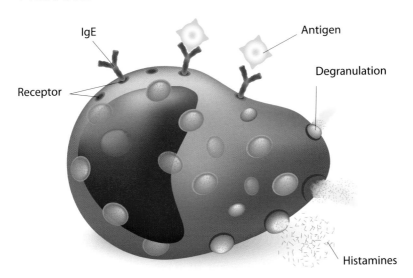

IgE

Antigen

Degranulation

Receptor

Histamines

Allergy – why me?

Allergies now affect about one in four of the UK population with people often having more than one allergic condition like hay fever, asthma and eczema. There is no one reason why people develop allergies but lots of contributing factors.

Factors contributing to the development of allergy

- The person's genetic make-up
  - How T cells respond
  - More common in boys than girls
  - Having one parent who has allergy makes a child three to six times more likely to develop an allergy than a child with non-allergic parents
- The age that you first come into contact with the allergen (children are more likely to develop allergies than adults)
- How you come into contact with the allergen e.g. breathing it or eating it
- What other things are stimulating the immune system
- Socioeconomic status
- Family size
- Early childhood infections
- Atmospheric pollution
- Nutrition
- Diesel fumes
- Geography
- Living in a very "clean" environment

Vinca minor
Photographer: Henry Oakeley

Nigella damascena
Photographer: Clive Nichols

Chapter Two

How do we investigate
and diagnose allergies?

Chapter Two

How do we investigate and diagnose allergies?

The number of patients needing allergy testing is increasing. It is important to remember that the severity of symptoms of allergy can vary considerably. Some people clearly have an allergy but their symptoms are mild and inconvenient and can be managed using over the counter treatments and without going to see their doctor. However, there are situations when it is important that patients are thoroughly investigated – these are shown in the table below.

When should you consult your doctor if you have an allergy?

- If you have severe symptoms e.g. anaphylaxis
- If your symptoms are affecting your overall health
- If you have progressively worsening symptoms
- If you think you have an allergy to something that is difficult to exclude (e.g. milk or eggs)
- If the suspected allergen relates to your work
- If you show a severe reaction to a particular tree or plant
- If you are allergic to your pet

Any investigation must start with a careful history taking, asking about the possible allergens which may be involved, what type of symptoms are occurring, what time of the year they occur etc. Some of the important points in the history are shown on page 32. If you think you have an allergy, tell your GP about the symptoms you are having, when they happen, how often they occur and if anything seems to trigger them. Your GP can offer advice and treatment for mild allergies. If you need allergy testing or specialist advice, you may be referred to an allergy clinic. If you have a severe or complex allergy, you may need to be seen at one of the larger allergy centres. A professional organisation called the British Society for Allergy and Clinical Immunology has a website that gives information of where to find local NHS allergy services. http://www.bsaci.org/find-a-clinic/index.htm

Trachelospermum jasminoides
Photographer: Henry Oakeley

The important points to note in the history

- **Age**
  - Children are more likely to develop allergies
  - Babies and young children should be investigated by people with paediatric training
  - Allergies can have a wider impact on children
    - Loss of schooling
    - Poor health
    - Exclusion from normal activities e.g. outdoor sports

- **Family history**
  - Positive family history increases the likelihood of allergy in an individual
- **Symptoms**
  - What symptoms and where e.g. respiratory tract, eyes, skin
- **Severity of symptoms**
  - Mild and inconvenient or severe, life changing
- **Time of symptoms**
  - All year
  - Seasonal – which months?
- **When symptoms occur**
  - Daytime/nighttime
- **Where symptoms occur**
  - Indoors/outdoors
  - By particular plants/trees

An important test used in diagnosing asthma is measuring the peak flow of air out of the lungs. A characteristic of asthma is variable peak flow, usually between morning and evening measurements. Patients who are treated for asthma should see an improvement and a reduction in variability of the peak flow readings. More detailed lung function tests are available for more complex patients. Allergy testing is important to find out whether a patient's asthma is associated with inhaled allergens.

Begonia grandis
Photographer: Henry Oakeley

Pollen calendar

If you have hay fever or seasonal rhinitis, the time of year when symptoms are most severe is one of the most important pieces of information to help identify the allergens that someone may be reacting to. Tree pollens appear in late January with a peak in March-April. By May, the tree pollen is reducing but the grass pollen is starting, peaking in June. Finally, the weed pollens appear in June and July. The pollen calendar shows the general situation for the UK but more detailed information including day-to-day pollen forecast can be found at
http://www.metoffice.gov.uk/health/public/pollen-forecast

Testing for allergy

There are two general ways of investigating allergy but they are only useful if they are used alongside a good clinical history and examination. Skin prick testing and IgE measurement (total and specific) are both commonly used and each has advantages and disadvantages. In reality, both methods of investigation have a role in the allergy clinic and, when appropriate, an allergist will use a combination depending upon the patient's age, symptoms, the allergens and the overall clinical picture.

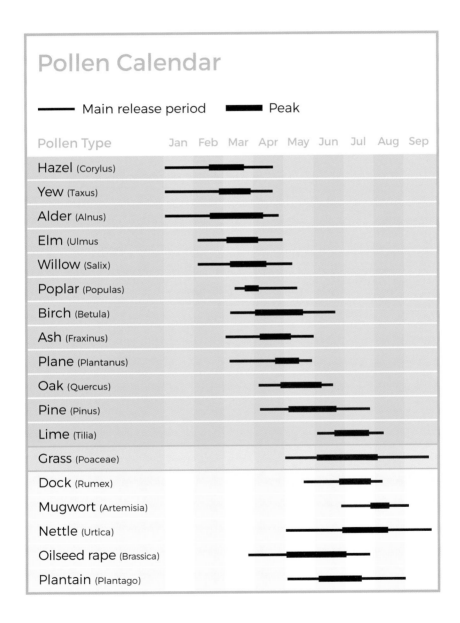

Pollen Calendar

—— Main release period   ▬▬ Peak

Pollen Type	Jan	Feb	Mar	Apr	May	Jun	Jul	Aug	Sep
Hazel (Corylus)									
Yew (Taxus)									
Alder (Alnus)									
Elm (Ulmus)									
Willow (Salix)									
Poplar (Populas)									
Birch (Betula)									
Ash (Fraxinus)									
Plane (Plantanus)									
Oak (Quercus)									
Pine (Pinus)									
Lime (Tilia)									
Grass (Poaceae)									
Dock (Rumex)									
Mugwort (Artemisia)									
Nettle (Urtica)									
Oilseed rape (Brassica)									
Plantain (Plantago)									

Citrus x limon
Photographer: Henry Oakeley

Skin prick testing (SPT)

Skin prick testing is an easy way of determining whether a person has an allergic response to a specific allergen. It is usually done in an allergy clinic by specially trained staff and is a simple, safe and quick test (results are usually available within about 20 minutes).

Abelia x grandiflora
Photographer: Henry Oakeley

Skin prick testing (SPT) process

- The SPT is usually done on the inner forearm. If a larger area of skin is needed e.g. for SPT in a baby or young child, or if the patient has eczema on their arm, other areas of the body may be used e.g. back or thigh.
- The test allergens are selected based on the patient's history.
- As few as three or four or up to about 25 allergens can be tested at one time.
- The skin is labelled with a soft pen to identify which allergens are placed where.
- A drop of the pre-prepared allergen solution is placed on the skin.
- The skin is then pricked through the drop using the tip of a special blunt lancet – this should not hurt and should not bleed.
- The skin prick test introduces a tiny amount of allergen into the skin. If the patient reacts to the allergen, mast cells will degranulate, releasing inflammatory mediators where the allergen was pricked into the skin. This generates a small, local allergic response of a wheal (bump) and flare (redness).
- Control samples must be included in every SPT. A positive control should cause a reaction in all people and a negative control should not cause a reaction in anyone.
- The size of the wheal and flare reactions are measured and compared to the positive control reaction.

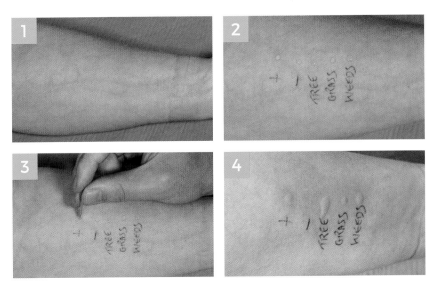

1. Arm before test. 2. Spots of test allergens placed on the skin.
3. The skin is pricked through the drop. 4. Wheal and flare reaction.

There are some limitations to SPT. The results are unreliable if the patient is taking antihistamine medications so antihistamines should be stopped for between two and five days before the SPT (depending on the antihistamine preparation). The SPT should not hurt but the skin may become itchy, red and swollen within a few minutes but this subsides within about one hour. Negative SPT may indicate that the patient is not sensitive to that allergen but negative reactions do occur for other reasons. Some patients, particularly if they react to lots of allergens, may have a positive SPT but describe encountering that allergen without any symptoms. These false negative and false positive results make it vital that results are interpreted with the patient's history. There is also a very small chance that a patient will have a severe reaction to the SPT therefore resuscitation facilities should be available in clinics where SPT is done.

Begonia grandis
Photographer: Henry Oakeley

Choysia ternata
Photographer: Clive Nichols

People doing SPT will have been fully trained, nevertheless, the results can be variable between operators. The advantages of SPT are that the results are available within minutes and the testing can be done and the results interpreted at one clinic appointment. The results are visible and a patient will be able to see themselves what allergens they are responding to. SPT evaluates a person's response to allergens *in vivo* and is likely to be representative of "real life".

Total and specific IgE

Measurement of total IgE and specific IgE (IgE with reactivity against specific allergens) in the blood is central to the laboratory diagnosis of allergy. These tests are done in pathology laboratories by fully trained doctors, clinical scientists and biomedical scientists. The laboratories have a rigorous process of accreditation to ensure that they have everything in place to generate reliable and useful test results.

Diagnostic and pharmaceutical companies have spent years perfecting the technology to identify and purify specific allergens from their source material. A useful website for learning more about total and specific IgE testing can be found at http://www.thermoscientific.com/en/products/allergy-diagnostic-systems-products.html

The technology and automation used for IgE testing have improved over time but the basic method remains the same. Allergens are purified from raw materials e.g. birch or grass pollens. The purification process is carefully controlled so the

Hemerocallis
Photographer: Clive Nichols

antigen stays as close to its native state as possible. The purified allergens either individually or as an allergen mix, are bound onto an unreactive sponge. This sponge is approximately 3mm in diameter by 2mm thick and has a huge surface area to maximise allergen binding. The sponges are put into small cups and are then packed into carrying tubes for quality checking and distribution to testing laboratories.

The actual analysis is automated and involves the patient's blood sample being added to the small cup containing the allergen-coated sponge. There is one cup for every allergen (or allergen mix) being tested. The sample is incubated and during this time, any IgE in the patient's sample with reactivity against the allergen on the sponge will bind to the allergen.

The next step is to wash away the remaining sample and IgE that has not bound to the allergen on the sponge. An antibody that binds onto the IgE molecule is added and will stick to any IgE that is bound to the allergen on the sponge. This anti IgE has a special fluorescent tag on it.

The final stage is reading the amount of fluorescence in the cup, which reflects how much specific IgE against that particular allergen is in the patient's sample.

The total and specific IgE testing process is much more objective than SPT. There is an International Reference Preparation for IgE and results are reported as kilo units per litre (kU/L) of total IgE or specific IgE. Laboratories participate in external quality assurance schemes to check that their results are comparable to those of other laboratories across the country, so that test results from different laboratories can be compared.

We interpret laboratory tests by comparing them to the reference range. These are the values expected for a healthy person. Raised total IgE concentrations are not only seen in allergic disease. They may also be found in patients with parasitic infections, immune deficiencies, malignancies, liver disease and some viral infections. The IgE concentration does not directly relate to the severity of an allergy.

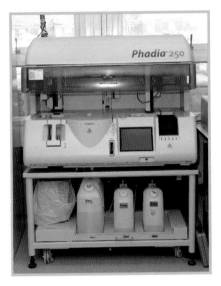

A laboratory machine for testing for IgE

However, a raised total IgE concentration suggests a high risk of allergic disease. An IgE concentration within the reference range (particularly in children) does not exclude significant allergy and if there are strong clinical indications, further investigation is warranted. The number of kU/L can be converted into broad groups or grades which can be used as a guide to the patient's potential reactivity to an allergen (or types of allergens). The specific IgE concentration, grades and possible significance are shown on page 47. However, like total IgE, the specific IgE does not necessarily correlate with disease activity.

Aloysia citriodora
Photographer: Henry Oakeley

Interpretation of Specific IgE

Units kU/L	Grade	Interpretation/Significance
<0.35	0	Negative
· Grades 1-3 - vary in significance depending on the allergen · Positive specific IgE indicates that a patient has the POTENTIAL to react to an allergen		
0.37 - 0.7	1	Weak positive Grade 1 to foods or moulds may be significant, to inhaled allergens is of doubtful significance
0.7 - 3.5	2	Positive
3.5 - 17.5	3	Positive
17.5 - 50	4	Strong positive
50 - 100	5	Strong positive
>100	6	Strong positive

The British Society for Allergy and Clinical Immunology does not recommend allergy testing for IgE at a distance or by untrained individuals. It does not advise the use of unproven tests such as kinesiology, Vega tests or hair analysis to investigate allergies.

Astrantia major
Photographer: Clive Nichols

Chapter Three

What allergies and when?

Chapter Three

What allergies and when?

The amount of pollen being released changes during the day. Pollen counts are highest early in the morning (between 5 am and 10 am) when the pollen is being released and in the evening when the air cools and pollens that have been carried up into the air begin to fall to ground level again. The best time to go out is after rain, which helps clear pollen from the air. Up-to-date information about the pollen count is easily available in newspapers, on the radio and television and the Met Office has up-to-date pollen counts by region.
http://www.metoffice.gov.uk/health/public/pollen-forecast

We have shown how the pollen calendar can be used as an initial indication as to the source of someone's respiratory allergy but simply looking at what plants are in flower at any time gives big clues about what pollen is around. Grass pollens are the most common seasonal allergen with peak grass pollen season between May and July but trees (January to May) and weeds (June to September) are also important. Knowing what allergen(s) you react to can be very helpful in managing them. There are some fairly simple measures that can be taken to reduce allergen exposure during the pollen season:

Strategies to avoid your allergen triggers and allergy symptoms

- Monitor pollen and mould counts
- Keep windows closed when indoors
- Plan your outdoor activities when the pollen count is lower
- Stay inside on dry, windy days
- Take a shower, wash your hair and change your clothes after you've been working or playing outdoors
- Try to avoid mowing the lawn or keep lawns regularly mown to stop them flowering and producing pollen
- If you do need to mow the lawn or do other gardening activities, wear a NIOSH-rated 95 filter mask
- Take appropriate medication beforehand
- Don't hang laundry outside — pollen can stick to sheets and towels
- If high pollen counts are forecast start taking allergy medications before your symptoms start
- Close doors and windows at night or when pollen counts are high
- Apply an effective allergen barrier around the edge of each nostril to trap or block pollens. Allergen barriers are available as balms or nasal sprays and some people have found petroleum jelly can help
- Wear wraparound sunglasses when outdoors to keep pollen out of your eyes
- A hat with a peak or large brim can help keep pollens from your eyes and face
- Pollen counts tend to be high along roads with grass verges (dual-carriageways, motorways). Keep car windows closed and the air intake on 're-circulate' when driving
- Choose a car that is fitted with an effective pollen filter, or get an in-car air filter

Penstemon
Photographer: Clive Nichols

Vitis vinifera
Photographer: Henry Oakeley

Treatments that prevent or suppress the symptoms of pollen-related allergies

If your allergy symptoms seem to be related to the pollen seasons, you may want to ask your pharmacist what over the counter treatments are available. However, if your symptoms are severe or if they do not improve with over the counter medication, then you should discuss them with your GP. All treatments for pollen-related allergies are best started before the symptoms start and should be taken regularly. It is much more difficult to control symptoms that are already well established so it is suggested that preventative treatment e.g. nasal sprays are started approximately two weeks before the pollen season is due to start and then as recommended by your GP or pharmacist. Taking medications occasionally or when the symptoms are worst is much less effective than taking them regularly and as prescribed.

> ## There are a number of over the counter medications. These include:
>
> - Antihistamine
> - Steroid (corticosteroid) drops and nasal sprays
> - Nasal decongestants
> - Eye drops

It is important that you read the instructions that come with your medication, as using them incorrectly increases your risk of developing side effects.

Digitalis purpurea
Photographer: Henry Oakeley

Antihistamines

Antihistamines block the action of histamine – the chemical released from mast cells during degranulation. They are usually effective at treating itching, sneezing and watery eyes, but they may not help to reduce a blocked nose. You can get antihistamines as tablets, nasal sprays and eye drops. There are different types of antihistamines with the more modern ones having a lower risk of causing drowsiness. You can use antihistamines when you first notice you're developing the symptoms of hay fever or as a preventative treatment e.g. if you know that the pollen count is going to be high.

If you do become drowsy after using antihistamines, you must avoid driving or using heavy tools or machinery. You should also contact your GP or pharmacist, as there may be an alternative antihistamine you can take.

Thymus herba-barona
Photographer: Henry Oakeley

Steroid (corticosteroid) drops and nasal sprays

Steroid drops and nasal sprays that are used to treat hay fever have an anti-inflammatory effect which helps "damp down" the symptoms. Steroids are better than antihistamine tablets at preventing and relieving nasal symptoms, including sneezing and congestion. They can also relieve itchy, watery eyes. They are most effective if you start using them a couple of weeks before your symptoms begin and when used regularly during the pollen season.

GPs may prescribe steroid nasal sprays or drops for a short time for patients who have hay fever that doesn't respond to antihistamines, or if the main symptom is a blocked nose. They can as act a "local" treatment (just in the nose) for patients who are pregnant or breastfeeding.

Steroid (corticosteroid) tablets

In particular situations, your GP may prescribe a short course (approximately one week) of steroid tablets. This will be if you need quick, short-term relief from severe symptoms e.g. if you have an examination at peak pollen time.

Nasal decongestants

A decongestant nasal spray can relieve the blocked nose symptoms which are associated with hay fever. Decongestants reduce the swelling of the blood vessels in your nose, which opens your nasal passages and makes breathing easier. You can get nasal decongestants from your pharmacy or your GP can prescribe them but they should only be used in the short term e.g. for a few days.

Coleonema 'Sunset Gold'
Photographer: Henry Oakeley

Aquilegia vulgaris
Photographer: Henry Oakeley

Aquilegia vulgaris
Photographer: Clive Nichols

Eye drops

The red, itchy, watery eyes associated with hay fever can be treated with eye drops that are available from your pharmacist. Some preparations contain antihistamine, which will reduce the inflammation in your eyes. Other preparations contain a chemical called sodium cromoglycate, which reduces the chemical release from mast cells and therefore reduces symptoms.

Dicentra
Photographer: Clive Nichols

Immunotherapy

Immunotherapy can be a life-changing treatment for people with the most severe allergy symptoms that do not respond to any other treatments. Immunotherapy involves gradually introducing a patient to a small amount of the allergen e.g. pollen in a very controlled environment in order to desensitise the patient. Immunotherapy must be done in specialist allergy centres because serious allergic reactions (anaphylaxis) may occur. The allergen may be given as an injection into your skin or as a tablet that dissolves under your tongue. Patients are most closely monitored after the first doses of immunotherapy.

Immunotherapy should be started three months before the pollen season so patients can build up their tolerance to the allergen. During this time, the amount of allergen given will gradually be increased. The most successful treatments take three years and should give long-term pollen desensitisation. Immunotherapy does not work in everyone and if there is no significant improvement in symptoms after one year, then the treatment is unlikely to help and shouldn't be continued.

Leptospermum scoparium
Photographer: Henry Oakeley

Thalictrum aquilegiifolium
Photographer: Clive Nichols

Arbutus unedo
Photographer: Clive Nichols

Chapter Four

Other allergies related to plants

Chapter Four

Other allergies related to plants

Oral allergy syndrome

Oral allergy syndrome (also called pollen food syndrome) is itchiness, tingling and swelling of the mouth or throat after eating raw fresh fruit, nuts or vegetables. It is usually seen in people who are allergic to pollen from trees, grasses or weeds because their immune systems recognise some of the proteins in the foods as very similar to the proteins in the pollens. Birch pollen is most commonly associated with the oral allergy syndrome in the UK and patients may experience mouth itching and tingling when eating any of the foods shown in the table on page 69. Many of the proteins associated with these reactions are denatured by heating so people have no symptoms when they eat the cooked fruit or vegetable.

Begonia
Photographer: Clive Nichols

Begonia sutherlandii
Photographer: Henry Oakeley

Prunus x cistena
Photographer: Clive Nichols

Foods and pollens associated with the oral allergy syndrome

Birch pollen allergy	Grass pollen allergy	Weed pollen allergy
Fruits		
Apple	Kiwi	Apple
Apricot	Melon	Banana
Cherry	Orange	Melon
Kiwi	Tomato	
Mango	Watermelon	
Nectarine		
Peach		
Pear		
Plum		
Tomato		
Vegetables		
Carrot	Pea	Carrot
Celery	Potato	Celery
Fennel	Swiss chard	Coriander
Onion		Fennel
Parsley		Parsley
Parsnip		Parsnip
Potato		
Spinach		
Others		
Almond	Wheat	Honey
Brazil nut		Peanut
Hazel nut		Sunflower seeds
Honey		
Peanut		
Walnut		
Wheat		

Allergies to foods of plant origin

When we are talking about pollen allergies, we are mainly thinking about allergens that we breathe in. The oral allergy syndrome is an indirect response to pollen allergies that can be experienced when people eat particular foods.

There is another group of allergies that are caused directly by foods; these foods can be from animals e.g. milk, eggs, meat or fish but foods from plants are also important allergens.

Peanut, tree nuts and wheat are the most common foods that cause allergies but any plant food has the potential to be allergenic. The symptoms can range from mild and irritating to severe e.g. anaphylaxis.

Papaver
Photographer: Clive Nichols

Cotoneaster
Photographer: Clive Nichols

Papaver rhoeas
Photographer: Henry Oakeley

The principles of investigating food allergies are the same as for respiratory allergies with a good clinical history and patient examination being of major importance. Keeping a food diary that records what foods were eaten, whether there were any symptoms and what type of symptoms occurred is extremely useful in helping to identify the cause of the allergy. Skin prick testing and specific IgE testing can also support the clinical diagnosis.

Food allergies are also interesting because of the similarities in the protein components of closely related plants. For example, people who are allergic to peanuts may also experience symptoms when they eat peas, lentils or beans (all members of the legume family). Similarly, people who are allergic to Brazil nuts may experience symptoms when eating other tree nuts like walnuts or cashews. People who are allergic to melons may have symptoms when they eat bananas, avocado or kiwi. This is called cross reactivity and some knowledge of which plants are related to each other can be very helpful in identifying the cause of allergies.

There are other types of immune reactions that cause sensitivities to foods. A good example is coeliac disease where the immune response is to gluten (mainly from wheat). The symptoms of coeliac disease include diarrhoea, stomach pains, weight loss and tiredness but can affect any part of the body. Coeliac disease is caused by T cells and not by IgE so the symptoms take longer to appear and it is not associated with anaphylaxis.

Skin allergies caused by plants

Plants can also cause dermatitis - the general name for skin irritation, which includes itching, rashes, blisters, redness, hives and dry flaky skin. People like gardeners, florists or chefs who have frequent contact with plants and fruit or vegetables have an increased chance of developing dermatitis. The symptoms can be because a person has an allergic reaction to the plant although the process is slightly different to hay fever and food allergy.

Plants may also contain irritating spines and chemicals that cause a reaction on the skin after contact with the plant. These reactions can be made worse by exposure to sunlight.

Hairs, spikes or spines are parts of plants' normal structures – they can range from small fine hairs to large sharp spikes. If they get lodged in the skin, they can directly cause skin irritation. Plants can also contain irritant chemicals that are released onto the skin on contact. Stinging nettles have hairs that break off when touched and these tiny "needles" deliver chemicals like formic acid and histamine into the skin. Histamine is the same chemical that causes allergy symptoms. Calcium oxalate, saponins and cyanogenic glycosides are other common chemical irritants found in plants. We are probably most familiar with capsaicin found in chilli peppers, which can cause acute redness and burning if it comes into contact with delicate skin e.g. around the eyes. These reactions are not generated by the immune system so everyone is affected in a similar way.

Allergic dermatitis is an immune reaction where T cells recognise an allergen and cause skin symptoms. These reactions take longer to appear than an IgE-mediated reaction and are

Punica granatum
Photographer: Henry Oakeley

Hemerocallis
Photographer: Clive Nichols

Geum rivale
Photographer: Henry Oakeley

called delayed hypersensitivity reactions. Poison ivy is the classical plant that causes allergic dermatitis but the ivy found in the UK does not contain the same chemicals so does not cause the same symptoms. Plants of the daisy (Compositae) family can also cause allergic contact dermatitis. The active chemical is called sesquiterpene lactone and is found in the leaves, flowers, hairs and stems of sunflowers, dandelion, ragweed and chrysanthemums and causes chronic redness and itching in people who are sensitive. Hogweed, carrot, celery, lime, lemon and grapefruit sap all contain chemicals (furocoumarins) that are sensitive to light. If the sap comes into contact with the skin and sunlight, the chemicals become activated and red, swollen, painful blisters appear within about 24 hours and there can even be longer term skin darkening.

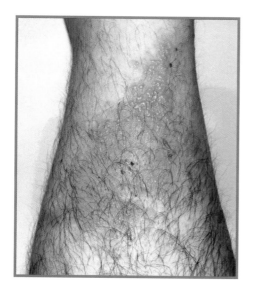

Typical rash of allergic contact dermatitis that is caused by a reaction to the chemicals in the plant's leaves, stems, flowers or roots.

Some plants that are known to cause contact dermatitis

- Primula
- Tulip bulbs
- Onion
- Garlic
- Dahlia
- Parsnip

- Celery
- Parsley
- Fennel
- Orange
- Chrysanthemum
- Feverfew

Papaver rhoeas
Photographer: Henry Oakeley

There are many plants that are potentially harmful to people either because they are poisonous or cause contact skin symptoms. A comprehensive list of these plants is on the RHS website: https://www.rhs.org.uk/advice/profile?PID=524#section-4

Ajuga reptans
Photographer: Clive Nichols

Alchemilla mollis
Photographer: Clive Nichols